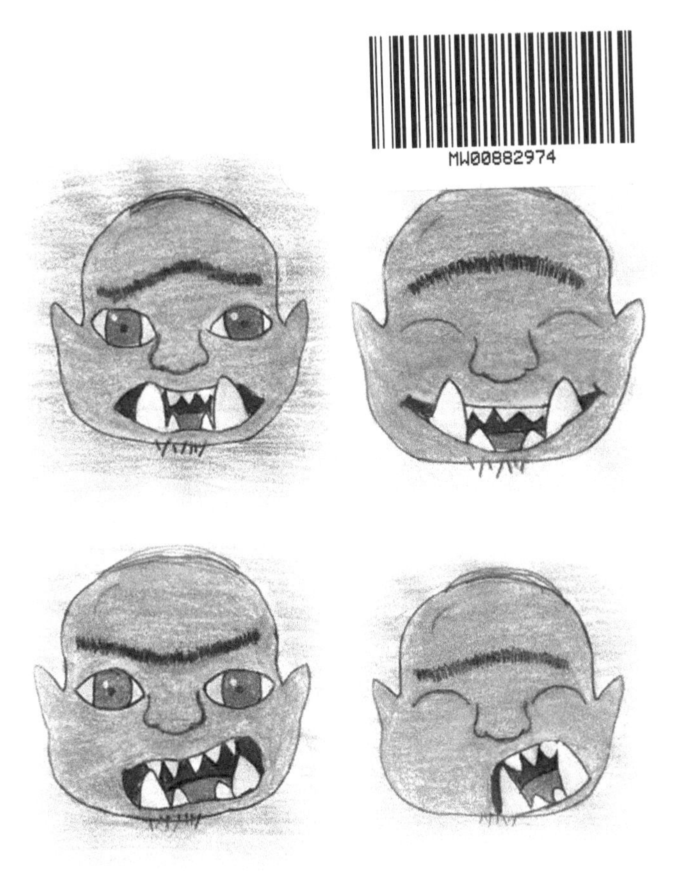

The Explorer's Guide to Ogre Faces

Written By: Adam Ross
Illustrated By: Violet Ross

Welcome Explorers!

Thank you for accepting this quest! Reading will open doors to countless new adventures. A bit of advice before embarking on this particular quest:

The use of Total Physical Response (TPR) will aid in memory retention. So, have the reader(s) practice the faces with the emotions as they read and work through the Spell Scrolls section in the back. One of biggest triggers for emotional outbursts in children is a lack of ability to accurately describe how they are feeling. Hopefully, this will help provide a safe ground for building that vocabulary.

This first book is dedicated to my family. From my kids, Elisabeth and Connor, my parents, brother, sister-in-law, to my niece and nephews. Without your support and encouragement, these would all sit on a thumbdrive and be lost to time. I love you all.

This is an <u>ogre</u>.

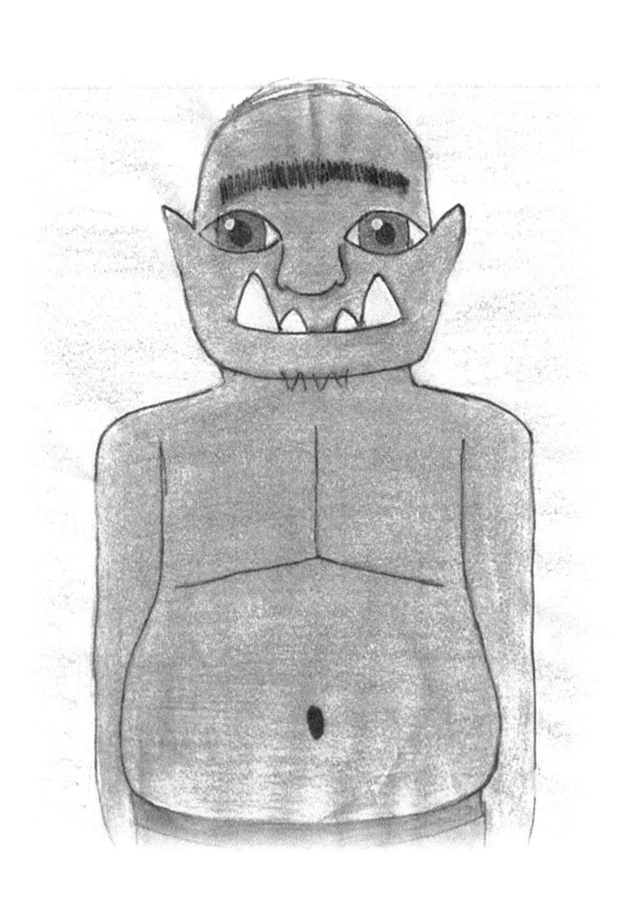

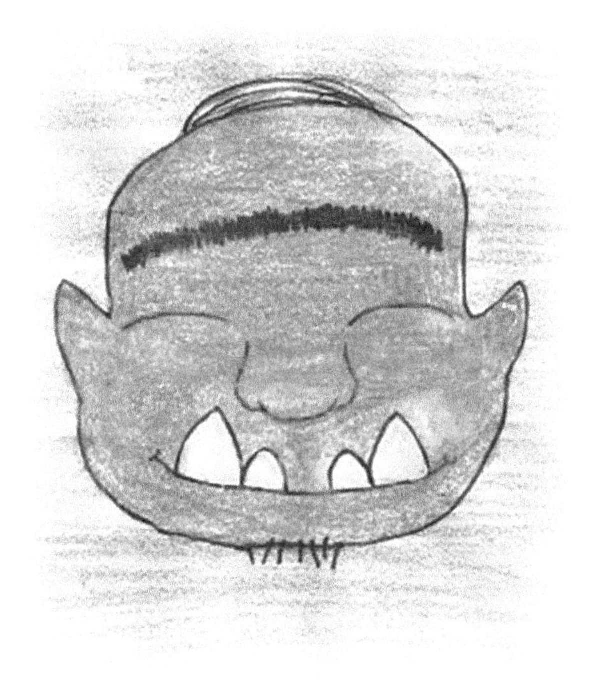

An ogre can be
<u>happy</u>.

An ogre can be sad.

An ogre can be
mad.

An ogre can be scared.

An ogre can be
excited.

An ogre can be
tired.

An ogre can be
sick.

An ogre can be hurt.

Spell Scrolls

Find the words hidden in the puzzle below.
Draw a line around each word as you find them.

J	T	V	E	S	R	E	B
H	U	R	T	C	A	X	D
A	L	X	S	A	D	C	V
P	B	D	W	R	Q	I	L
P	X	Y	U	E	I	T	P
Y	C	G	Z	D	H	E	M
S	I	C	K	Y	G	D	A
Q	W	P	T	I	R	E	D

SAD	HAPPY	MAD	EXCITED
TIRED	SICK	HURT	SCARED

Draw a line form the ogre's face to match how it feels. Then say the word.

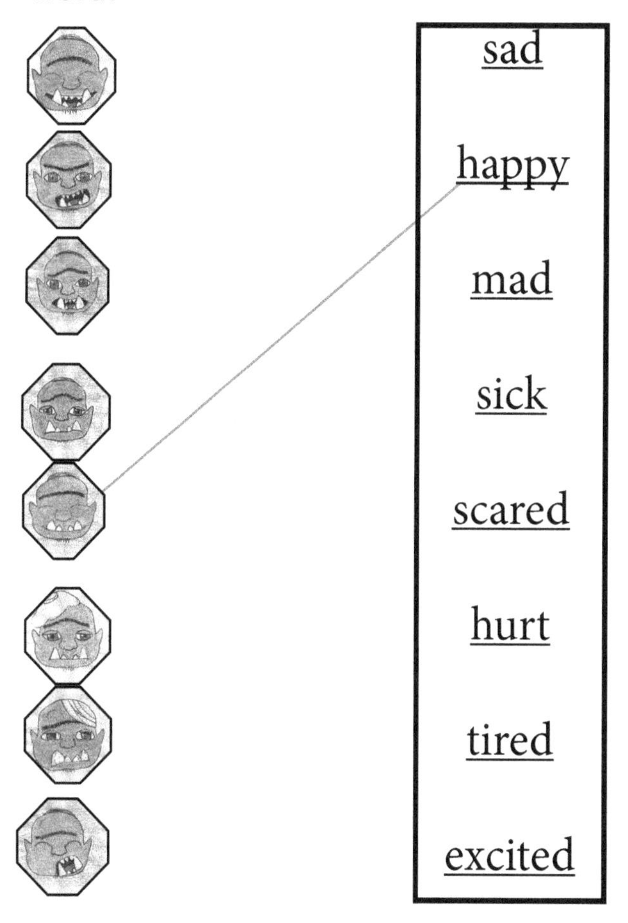

Trace and say each word. three times.

sad	sad	sad
happy	happy	happy
mad	mad	mad
tired	tired	tired
hurt	hurt	hurt
sick	sick	sick
scared	scared	scared
excited	excited	excited

Coming Soon!

Keep an eye out for these future titles soon to come!

- The Explorer's Guide to Swords, The Explorer's Guide to Shields, and The Explorer's Guide to Potions - These will help build a reader's vocabulary for describing relative sizes such as Thick/Thin, 2D Shapes, and basic Colors while also giving them baseline vocabulary for some of the items they will encounter in a fantasy setting.
- The Explorer's Guide to the Creatures of Luna Nueva & The Explorer's Guide to the Places of Luna Nueva - Will prepare readers for Level 2 books by building their vocabulary for the characters places that they will begin interact with in a Fantasy setting.
- A Quilt is Made of Pieces - A heartfelt rhyming book designed for Read Aloud that addresses how our differences make us unique and enhance the beauty of the world around us.
- Legends of Luna Nueva - At Level 3, Readers will get to dive into the Kingdom of Luna Nueva and begin their Reading Adventure! Following the young Patrons of Luna Nueva, readers will be encouraged to continually build on their skills as readers from vocabulary to comprehension and recall, eventually taking them all the way up to Teen Readers.

Violet Ross is a lover of fantasy. She mostly started drawing when she made a character for a TTRPG (Tabletop Roleplaying Game), and wanted to design it. When she was given the opportunity to illustrate a fantasy book, she almost immediately took the offer. Violet used watercolor and colored pencils to illustrate the book, for good coverage throughout her drawings.

Adam Ross is the founder and primary author of First Fantasy Books. He earned his Master of Arts in Teaching, and taught for six years before starting on this passion project. During his time teaching, he witnesed students struggling to engage with the content they were being offered, especially in Early English Readers. He wanted to create content that was entertaining as well as developmentally appropriate. With these books, Adam hopes to encourage a love of reading, emotional awareness, and a sense of belonging for all readers.

CPSIA information can be obtained
at www.ICGtesting.com
Printed in the USA
BVHW020738110222
628583BV00024B/504